LOBO

BOOKS BY MacKINLAY KANTOR

Fiction

DIVERSEY · EL GOES SOUTH · THE JAYBIRD

LONG REMEMBER · THE VOICE OF BUGLE ANN

AROUSE AND BEWARE · THE ROMANCE OF ROSY RIDGE

THE NOISE OF THEIR WINGS · HERE LIES HOLLY SPRINGS

VALEDICTORY · CUBA LIBRE · GENTLE ANNIE

HAPPY LAND · AUTHOR'S CHOICE · GLORY FOR ME

MIDNIGHT LACE · WICKED WATER · THE GOOD FAMILY

ONE WILD OAT · SIGNAL THIRTY-TWO · DON'T TOUCH ME

WARWHOOP · THE DAUGHTER OF BUGLE ANN

GOD AND MY COUNTRY · ANDERSONVILLE

Juvenile

ANGLEWORMS ON TOAST

LEE AND GRANT AT APPOMATTOX

GETTYSBURG

Autobiographical

BUT LOOK, THE MORN

Verse

TURKEY IN THE STRAW

LOBO

by

MacKinlay Kantor

ILLUSTRATED BY IRENE LAYNE

THE WORLD PUBLISHING COMPANY

CLEVELAND AND NEW YORK

PUBLISHED BY The World Publishing Company
2231 West 110th Street, Cleveland 2, Ohio

PUBLISHED SIMULTANEOUSLY IN CANADA BY
Nelson, Foster & Scott Ltd.

Library of Congress Catalog Card Number: 57–7407

FIRST EDITION

To
Caroline

LOBO

Wʜᴇɴ first we encountered him, he was disguised as a *fiesta*.

If ever I did know what particular Spanish historical occasion is celebrated on the night of February 15th, I have forgotten. It was on such a night.

The unique enterprise which Lobo had decided to grace with his presence is deemed the Montemar-El Remo complex. It is directed by the Marqués de Nájera, whose exploits on the golf courses of Andalucía vie with his hold on fame as a cavalry officer during the Rif campaigns. Angel, as he is called by intimates, is seconded in command by the lovely María Luisa Rein. From these people

LOBO

I learned eventually such details of Lobo's past as might have escaped the attention of ordinary biographers.

The Montemar Hotel is a sprawling white plaster building rambling along the shoulder of a hill, with the Mediterranean turning choicely blue or bitterly gray a quarter of a mile beneath. Down on those shores is the gayer portion of the concern: El Remo, a busy little restaurant by day, and by night a club where the light fantastic is tripped, and where on occasion a few of the light-minded fantastic individuals of the Gay International Set have indulged in earnest hair-pullings.

The cuisine, presided over by one Cristóbal, is above reproach if some of the guests occasionally aren't. Grouped near El Remo are cottages and a row of modern glass-fronted apartments, all a part of the same brave social scheme.

. . . A *fiesta* was in progress, and what with serpentine and confetti and noisemakers and champagne and brandy, everything was moving right well at two A.M.

By nature an abstemious man, I was not at all polluted. But my senses shivered as I watched a portion of the carnival scenery detach itself and move calmly toward us.

I murmured to my wife, "Do you see what I see?"

Irene said limply, "I guess we've had too many drinks. We ought to go home."

"Let's go—I'm with you. Serpentine doesn't just get up and walk around."

That is what the serpentine was doing. A huge parti-colored mound of the gay paper streamers progressed ominously across the dance floor.

"Serpentine's got a tail," we observed. Sure enough, the paper mountain did have a tail, a stubby sickle-shaped appendage with a white tip.

Cristóbal approached our table.

"Please, what is *that*?" We indicated the ambulatory hummock which now had turned majestically on another course.

"Ah, that. That is Lobo."

Thus began an acquaintance which ripened into friendship, which in turn ripened into obsession, which in turn ripened into madness. In the direction of Lobo (in Spanish, *wolf*) lay madness.

If you chose to introduce a Doberman, a German shepherd, and an old red-bone hound and have them somehow intermingle and beget, they might have produced something like Lobo. He had yellow eyes and droopy ears. His legs and feet were fawn-colored; and they were slim legs and tiny feet, although made of piano wire. Also tan was the mask across his face, which he wore flagrantly in a land where the wearing of masks is a felony. He had a white necktie; from this formal white decoration a pale zipper extended backward under his belly. Often I was possessed of the insane impulse to unzip that zipper but was too appalled at the notion of what I might find inside.

Lobo weighed an even fifty pounds on the dot. He could run about twice as fast as any greyhound at the Sarasota Kennel Club, at least any that I ever bet on. His teeth had been hand-forged in Seville by some master sword-smith; his tongue was a slice of palest *Serrano* ham; most of his body had been well blacked and rubbed by the best *limpiabotas* in Spain. (That is foreign talk for bootblack.)

According to Angel and María Luisa, Lobo's mother belonged to a shepherd in the hills behind the Montemar. This unhappy country matron presented the not-too-proud shepherd with a litter of puppies one cold day. The Spaniards are a philosophical race—also practical, if at times uncertain according to our standards in their moral motives. The practical and benevolent shepherd turned the puppies out to die. He said that he could feed no more dogs than the one. I suppose that most of them did die. Perhaps up there amid flint and boulders of the coastal range are lying the long-picked bones of Lobo's kin. No bones of Lobo are there.

Lobo betook himself shoreward. I can understand how his reasoning went, and so can anyone else who knew him.

"Let's see," Lobo meditated. "Shelter, of course—I don't like being rained on. . . . Food . . . yes, yes, but not ordinary food. Something exotic would be more to the point. . . . Companionship? For a certainty. And I do

like a place with an open fire and red leather cushions."

So he showed up at the most expensive café on the southern coast of Spain, and moved in as manager, a grade or two above the rank held later by Cristóbal.

How long since all this had taken place?

Time means very little to the Spanish.

You would say, "How long has Lobo been here?"

"Oh, for years."

"How many years?"

"Oh, for some years, *Señor*."

"Well, two years, three years?"

"Oh, yes."

"Four years, five years?"

The shrug. "Perhaps."

"Six years?"

"I don't know, *Señor*. He has been here for years."

Actually he had a few gray hairs when first we knew him. But a vet who looked at his teeth later said they were the teeth of a young dog. . . . *No lo sé, Señoras y Señores.*

Far from being the playboy type, he was a man of serious purpose, definitely community-minded. A native of the United States, he would have belonged—congenially, productively—to the Elks, the Masons or K of C, the Rotary Club, and probably the American Legion or the Veterans of Foreign Wars. (If a war had been going on, you wouldn't have been able to keep Lobo out of it.) A native of Spain, however, he belonged to no organization; although on good rumor he attended sessions of the Friends of New Torremolinos, the village booster organization—most especially if the meeting had a banquet attached.

He was known in every shop. All cooks and gardeners and maids knew him. The children knew him. The Civil Guards treated him with respect. "Good morning, Lobo," they would say. He would bow and continue on his course, which usually had something to eat at the end of it.

Most of the *turistas* who came to El Remo thought naturally that this beast belonged to Fermín or Antonio or Miguel or Cristóbal or Pedro or someone of the staff. At times the staff thought he belonged to the Devil. He was not in those days a cross dog. Neither was he a dirty dog, he was not a smelly dog; he did not jump up on the tables. Still the mere ubiquity of the creature was something to be contended with.

His comforts were eminently provided for at the café; the huge golden eyes did the trick. He was catholic as to his tastes. Often we saw him leisurely munching chicken bones contributed by some tot. He ate every variety of *hors d'oeuvre* in the place, although he was most partial to caviar.

His procedure consisted of approaching a table and putting his stony head on a knee or a lap. When you looked down to see what was this weight you were bearing, the weight was Lobo. You fed him, you had to, you couldn't *not* feed Lobo. That is, nineteen out of twenty people couldn't. The twentieth person (often a Swede or a German, with strict ideas as to the table deportment of dogs) would fly into a rage and flail with his napkin. Lobo sought neither to resist nor retaliate. He simply shrugged and strolled on to another table.

This is not champagne or brandy talk, Spanish. or otherwise; but it does seem that I have seen him eat at least twice his weight in anchovy olives, cold sausage, almonds, tuna fish, white bread, omelette, ice cream, pickled shrimp, candied cherries, and vegetable soup in a single evening. When even his rubber belly could hold no more, he would saunter toward a cushion on the built-in bench near the fireplace. If some interloper happened to be there, he would fling himself across the interloper's feet as a hint that the spot should be vacated.

Generally he was very even as to temper— again, in those days. From time to time he traveled with a troop of native dogs ambling about the neighborhood. He was larger than most, he seemed to rule by influence rather than by brawn. I never saw him in but one fight—in those days—and then it was with a snobbish French poodle who swished into the place and apparently whispered some slighting reference to Lobo's ancestry or background.

Being seated closest to the scene of strife, and having achieved by that time a working knowledge of Lobo, I managed to save the visiting poodle from complete dismemberment. . . .

"How *dare* you!" the poodle's mistress was shrieking in five languages. "How dare you retain such a wicked beast? You should keep your dog on leash!"

"Madam," I said, "he is not my dog." Suddenly my heart was a little heavy at the thought that this was true.

If Lobo had no family of his own it was not his fault. He was willing to have a family, he courted families. Did the mighty General Carlos Martínez Amadeo Silva y Serrano appear for a quiet holiday on the seashore, complete with *la señora*, nine children, and eleven maids? Lobo moved in with them. Invariably he was welcomed as a combination court jester, tutor, night watchman, and scullion. Then, the fortnight of seaside bliss being duly expended, the Silva tribe would return to Madrid minus Lobo.

The following week one of those same cottages might be occupied by an elderly countess, with whom Lobo would promptly effect a liaison. Next month it might be an ailing English couple, or an American painter, a Swiss professor, a Copenhagen merchant, a French opera singer. Lobo must have distributed more international affections than a Hollywood playboy on his first trip to the Riviera.

Thus he developed his allergy to suitcases. Lobo dissolved at the mere sight of a suitcase being dragged from its lair. His reaction was to depart into the nearest dark closet and lie with his face turned against his tail. When the suitcase was packed and closed, and a departure grew imminent, he froze even colder— he would not lift his head. He would not come out and say Goodbye, he would not display a brave heart in the face of separation. He would simply congeal until the *camareras* shoveled him out of the way when they came to prepare the abode for new tenants.

Later, when Lobo's life was identified with my own, other people used to come proudly and declare that they too had dwelt in such intimacy. "You know, Lobo lived with *us* once. For three weeks." They seemed confident of securing prestige by the statement.

The night we returned to Spain in the early spring of 1954 for our second period of residence, we entered El Remo. Lobo greeted us with open paws. We had planned to take a house that year, probably down the coast a little farther. Angel arranged temporary quarters for us in one of the glassy apartments on the shore; without invitation, Lobo accompanied us thither when we withdrew from the table.

This apartment had been occupied until the

previous week by the John Steinbecks, and I do not think that Lobo lived with them. Lobo did not like gypsies, or sadly enough, beggar children, since the latter element had been unkind to him in his infancy, and he had reason to remember cuffs, kicks, and hurtful stones. Beggar children gave him a wide berth. They would not have approached the Steinbeck establishment had Lobo been in occupancy. Mr. Steinbeck, however, is a resourceful man. He proceeded to get rid of the beggars whenever they came hissing outside the window with that supreme persistence known only to Andalucian mendicants. Mr. Steinbeck could speak no Spanish, but would erupt from his dwelling suddenly, screaming in English, "Buttered toast!" This had become a part of neighborhood tradition. It served well. Promptly the landscape would be overwhelmed with fast-fleeing brats. . . .

Lobo did exude an air of having been there

before, when he trotted into the apartment. Carefully he selected the best portion of the upholstered couch, curled up, winked at us, went to sleep. He was still there in the morning, motionless, and did not even deign to stretch—until breakfast was brought and there was some reason for getting up. He took his usual continental breakfast of buttered roll and marmalade, then asked me to open the door for him. He disappeared. We did not see him again until ten o'clock at night, when the very earliest-dining Spaniards begin to gather. Then he consumed dinner along with us, and moved in again for the night.

On the third day we were invited to a party. It was to be a large assemblage, and common sense and a certain degree of sophistication suggested that we should decline. The hostess was a member of the Gay International Set— by no means one of the hair-pullers—but still there were bound to be the usual Hollywood types, Left Bank types, Monaco types, Costa Brava types, with a good prospect of several people plunging fully clad into the swimming pool before the night was over.

Few diners were present when we walked into El Remo about ten or a little later, and certainly there was no Lobo in sight.

"Where is Lobo?" I asked.

"*Don* MacKinlay, he has gone to the party. Were you not invited to the party? Everyone has gone to the party."

We chattered out something about still being weary from our trip.

"Oh, yes," said Cristóbal. "I know that Lobo is there, because he saw them fetching in the food very early, and preparing tables in the Contessa's patio. He went up there immediately."

This night Lobo had decided to cast discretion to the winds, to become in name and deed one of the G.I.S. It was four o'clock A.M., and we were sound asleep, when the most horrible caterwauling burst forth outside our door, punctuated by a scratching assault on the panel. I arose and opened the door. Lobo staggered in. He had had too much to drink as well as too much to eat. He barely made it to the couch, and didn't get up until noon.

We started explaining suitcases to him a couple of days later.

"You see, Lobo, we have taken a house about five *kilómetros* down the beach, and of course that is too far from El Remo for your comfort. So—"

But we were talking to thin air, because he had gone into the closet. There was just that shiny black rear with its four-leaf-clover design of tan at a strategic place; that was all we could see.

He didn't move, not even after we crowded our bags into the car.

Irene bent over him tenderly. "Lobo, aren't you even going to say goodbye?"

He did follow us into the yard, but after one look at the loaded car he lay down and turned his face away.

"I almost hate to leave him," Irene mourned as we drove off.

"Why, heavens. He wouldn't be happy anywhere else. El Remo is his *home*, the only place he knows," and I had almost convinced myself of this by the time we reached our new quarters on the precipice at La Verdad.

Following a few meals cooked over charcoal, we felt that since we were the proud possessors of a regular kitchen and a regular stove, we would try a little roasting or baking. Most Spanish stoves might be good for fogging up an Air Force Base to conceal it from visual attack by the enemy; ours was no exception. A storm of smoke drove us out. We left the windows open and fled to El Remo.

Promptly a solid head was dumped on each of our four knees in turn, and Lobo expressed his pleasure by gobbling most of our dinners. Then he disappeared; we presumed that he had gone among other tables to beg for further sustenance—as if he needed it!—and after a postprandial visit to the bar, we went out to our car. The windows had been left open; this was still the off season, with very few cars parked beside the café, and no such fripperies as parking-lot attendants and the like.

Lobo was seated in the car. He had no license, but he was in the driver's seat.

I shoved him over between us. "Let's take him home for a visit. Might be fun."

"Now, don't you start that," said Irene.

"Oh, what's the harm? He can visit us for a couple of days, and then we'll bring him back and dump him down here the next time we come. He'd much rather be *here* than *there*. Anyone knows that."

Anyone didn't know that. We dumped him in due course a few nights later. I was rather sick of having him under foot all the time, and I was busy working on *Andersonville*, and I didn't see how Lobo could help me very much. Accordingly we came back for a Sunday evening snack; once we had seen him retreat toward the patio to join dancers and

33

diners there, we tiptoed quietly to the car and drove away.

All he did was to go up to the big coastal highway, the main artery which bisects the hillside area between El Remo and the Montemar Hotel. He lay beside the road for two days and two nights. The *Guardia Civil* told me so later, for they saw him and wondered about it.

We started to drive in to Málaga. Our car stood out more or less in that land of few automobiles, most of them of darker hue. We were driving a sedan with a cream-colored body and rust-colored top; it could be spotted far away.

As we whirred past the intersection I saw a shape beside the road.

"Is that Lobo back there?"

Irene turned for a look through the rear window. "It is indeed Lobo back there. He is coming at exactly ninety miles per hour."

There were some trucks around, there was a flock of sheep to be circled. I didn't want to see Lobo mashed before our very eyes, so hastily I pulled over to the side of the road and slowed down. He overtook the car like Mr. John Landy passing somebody in a wheel chair. He took off in a running dive when he was about fifteen feet away. Fortunately the window by the driver's seat was open, because that was his target.

When a fifty-pound plummet of solid dog lands smack on your stomach and chest, you know that you have been hit.

He said to us, "I couldn't imagine where you'd gone! You weren't down at El Remo; but I decided that you'd be driving along the highway one of these times, so I just waited there. Thanks a lot for stopping."

We went groaning to Málaga, where I left Lobo incarcerated in the car under the watchful eyes of the little crippled public-parking-attendant, and found a store where I could buy a collar and a leash. I bought Lobo a fine red collar. He had never worn a collar; I thought the red would be gay. No, he had never worn a collar in his life, nor had he been on leash either, as far as we knew; but delicately he trod the crowded sidewalks, overseeing our shopping, as if he had a half-dozen diplomas from obedience schools. There was nothing to do now but to take him back to La Verdad, where he'd remain in residence until our departure.

During an interlude he visited the local veterinarian in Torremolinos, whose quarters and talents were more suited to the drenching of oxen than the conducting of a boarding kennel. We had promised to move over to Mallorca for some sixteen days, homework and all, and we just couldn't see lugging Lobo to Madrid and thence by air to the Balearic Islands.

"He'll be perfectly all right up there at that so-called vet's," I assured Irene and my conscience. "Anyway, I know he needs to be wormed, and he ought to have a rabies shot, and he should have a good scrubbing, because probably he's never had a good scrubbing. I know that he plunges into the sea now and then; but that's not like soap and elbow grease."

I left Lobo in the car outside the vet's, while I went in to explain. . . . A poor dog, I said. . . . A beggar dog who has adopted us temporarily. . . . I would like to leave him for a while, until our return. He needs to be wormed, bathed, etc. . . .

El veterinario listened sympathetically and suggested that I bring the dog inside. We appeared, at opposite ends of the leash. The vet's eyes widened with delight.

"Why, mercy sakes," he said, or the Andalucian equivalent thereof. "I thought you said this was a *poor* dog—an unknown! Why, this is *El Lobo*!"

. . . Our friend brooded a good deal while we were gone, according to later report. The vet said that he was *muy desconsolado*. Lobo awarded us a flattering reception on our return.

. . . We found that he was given to mysterious illnesses. He had a couple of them that summer—times when he would lie in a chair or on the floor and not move of his own volition for several days; and he would not eat a bite, and would drink nothing. Once I took him up to the vet's for examination; after his temperature was taken and found to be normal, the vet only shook his head and gave Lobo a *laxante*. The animal perked out of it in a couple of days, and went bounding about the cliffs again.

During this season Lobo began to realize

that he was become a man of substance. His disposition underwent a slight if corrosive change. For the first time he growled at the Civil Guard.

In Spain, quite sensibly, many of the guards dwell in family barracks, complete with wives and children. One of these establishments was on a hilltop directly across the road from our place at La Verdad. Hence it was customary for the guards, who at a later hour would have to report for duty at the central office in Tor-remolinos, to take up stations outside our gate-way, and there await the American who might drive toward the village on morning errands. Sometimes there was one man, sometimes two or three, all very handsome in neat green uni-forms, with Tommy guns slung amiably over their shoulders and black hats shining. It was Standing Operating Procedure for them to wait there, and Standing Operating Proce-

dure for me to stop, ask if they should like a
lift, and fling open the door. The first time I
did this, Lobo nearly flung himself out of it.
He had decided that the car was his, and he
saw no reason why the *policía* should take
over. I counseled him severely and he re-
mained quiet, but with ears up. A rumbling
growl moved in the caverns of his body as the
trim military figures climbed into the rear seat.

"Why, here is *El Lobo*," they said. "Lobo,
how are you today?"

Grrrrr.

They forgave him the slight without resent-
ment; probably they thought it was quite natural. One guard said, "Lobo is now very rich."

I told him firmly, "Lobo is not rich. He is
the same dog he always was."

"Ah, yes. But, *Señor*, he is rich by comparison. You see, Lobo had nothing before; now
he has a beautiful home, and of course a hand-

some large American car. Yes," he said con-
.tentedly, "Lobo is rich. *Es verdad*."

Grrrrr, said Lobo.

Also in this same month romance lifted her
pretty head. Romance appeared for shy and
tentative calls, which increased to daily fre-
quency as the summer season—and the lady's
own season—advanced. We didn't know her
name, we called her Perrita; she belonged to
some one of the guards across the way. She
was yaller-dog as to color, and owned somewhat the proportions of a mule deer, and stood
nearly as tall as one. The net result of this dis-
parity in stature was complete frustration on
the part of Lobo, no matter how willing he
was to achieve wedded bliss. Finally Perrita
gave up in disgust and married a taller dog
down the road. . . . Sometimes I've seen the
same thing happen in the human species: generally speaking, it seems unwise for shorter

men to fall in love with much taller women.

We began to hear rumors. "Is it true? Are you taking Lobo back to the United States when you return?"

"Nothing could be further from the truth."

"You should take him. He loves to be with you."

We felt that it would take more than a merely expressed preference on Lobo's part to compel us to submit to such an ordeal. An ordeal also would it be for him. We planned not to proceed directly to the United States, but to drive to Madrid, thence through the Pyrenees into France, all the way up through France; and we would leave the car at a seaport while we went—by boat, air, and train—to look after some business in England, Denmark, Germany.

"You think that would be a kindness to the dog?" I demanded witheringly of these self-appointed advisors. "Why, the poor thing would have to be shut up in a kennel, week after week."

. . . I had made a few tentative queries, and had even secretly consulted a book of rules and regulations at the consulate in Málaga. . . . Not much trick about getting him into the United States, in case we really wanted to do so. All he had to have was a rabies certificate, and a deposition of good health, signed by a doctor shortly before embarkation. Then, if he stood up under scrutiny of the Public Health Officer in New York (and didn't take a piece out of him) he could be admitted at once. It was entirely discretionary with the officer.

But in the meantime—

France he could get into: no trouble about that. In England, dogs must be quarantined for six months. No exceptions; not if you are Prince Philip himself.

"Just think of Lobo, accustomed to all this

45

freedom, bounding about the stone staircases and cliffs, scampering along the shore, jumping like an ibex from rock to rock. Think of his languishing in a French kennel! It's too hideous to contemplate. We certainly shall *not* take Lobo. He is very happy at El Remo; he has his friends; he has plenty to eat." Etc., etc.

Men and women propose, Lobos dispose.

Community opinion seemed to be about equally divided. Some people asserted staunchly that we were right—imprisonment would be a cruelty of the worst kind. Others said, wasn't it terrible for those Kantors to go away and abandon their dog?

Our dog, indeed. I scowled at Lobo and felt almost that he needed to be abandoned. "Far as that is concerned," I said with sternness one late summer's evening, "shouldn't tonight be the night?" We had just returned from a dinner party, and Irene was yawning.

I said, "I thought I'd go by El Remo, have a drink or two, and say goodbye to the staff. We've got dates every night until we leave, so we shan't be going back there for dinner. This is as good a night as any other to leave Lobo. Pack your bags, Lobo." Which feat Lobo performed by bounding into the car again and sitting up expectantly.

Irene reached in, put her arms around him, hugged and petted him, and then went quickly down the steps toward our house, going rapidly because she wanted neither Lobo nor me to see her cry.

During the few minutes it took us to drive along the highway I expatiated on the comforts and glories of that café which was in fact Lobo's hostelry. . . . The season was in full swing, the parking lot was filled with little cars, attendants darted here and there with flashlights. There was a uniformed boy outside the door, another cheerful greeter inside. The joint was certainly jumping.

Lobo made his usual recognition grunts. These were a series of piglike sounds which he had originated. They meant, "Oh yes, we're back *here*. I know this place. Yes, yes. Well, well." I used to ask him whether he thought he was dog or pig; but he would only give a lopsided glance and keep on grunting.

Lobo set a course for the patio where people were still dining, and I found the Marqués de Nájera at the bar. I told him of my plan. On this very night I would abandon Lobo; or, not liking the word *abandon* under the circumstances, I should say that I would *return* Lobo to his own domicile.

"Yes, yes, I quite agree with you," said the host. "A very good idea. He might cry around for a day two after you depart, but he will be much happier here than in a kennel."

Angel is not a drinking man, but I believe he recognized desperation in my attitude. We lingered for a time at the bar. The marques's pink face shone even pinker under his neatly clipped gray locks, he stabbed the air with his finger for emphasis. I tried to convince the marques, the marques tried to convince me, I tried to convince myself, that this thing was right. Best make a clean break. Deeds, not words, were needed to affirm and underline the process of getting rid of Lobo.

Cristóbal came by. His unoccupied moments are few, but I managed to grab him during one of them. I took him aside and folded into his palm—not exactly a king's ransom in *pesetas*, but at least a duke's.

"Lobo must lack for nothing this winter."

"*Don* MacKinlay," said Cristóbal, "Lobo has never lacked for anything."

"Nevertheless, he might get sick and need

LOBO

to go to the doctor. He might— Oh well, you
will take good care of him, won't you?"

"We do not take care of Lobo," said Cristóbal with dignity. "Lobo takes care of us."

I peered out on the pretty little lawn below
the orchestra's platform. All the regular Sat-
urday night celebrants were gathered, and as
usual there were newcomers and transients. I
saw familiar faces, familiar bald heads or pa-
tent leather ones. I saw María Luisa, her dark
eyes flashing as she danced; I saw the lawyer
from Málaga, the motion-picture director
from Barcelona.

Also I saw a black tail with a white tip, a tail
shaped like a sickle, moving casually among
farther tables. I turned away.

The marques had to join people at dinner.
We shook hands, embraced, parted. Cristóbal and I shook hands, embraced, parted. Antonio the musician took a break and came to
the bar. We shook hands, embraced, parted.

Well, I thought, you won't get anywhere this way. Come on, get moving. . . .

Quietly I went toward the outer door which opened upon a graveled driveway in the opposite direction from the patio. The inner doorman sprang forward. There was a frown between his brows.

"*Señor*, where is Lobo?"

"Lobo," I said, "is among the tables in the patio, and there he will remain. Shhhh."

Shhhh, repeated the inner doorman.

I descended the steps. The outer doorman, or doorboy (*Botones*, we call him there, since he wears many buttons on his uniform) came up, also frowning.

"But, *Señor*, have you not forgotten *El Lobo*?"

"I have not forgotten *El Lobo*," I said. "I can never forget him. Shhhh."

Shhhh, said *Botones*.

I went around through the dark driveway,

past innumerable little cars. The parking-lot attendant came up through the gloom, his light flashed.

"Ah, *Señor*! But where is the dog?"

"Shhhh," I said. "The dog is among the dancers and tables of food on the patio. Shhhh."

Shhhh, said the parking-lot attendant.

We moved upon my car through darkness. Now, with so many strangers about, so many transients at this height of season, it behooved anyone to keep his car locked.

The attendant flashed his light . . . *and who should be waiting there?* A beautiful line from Alfred Noyes. I remember that Noyes said it was Bess, the landlord's daughter, plaiting a dark red love-knot into her long black hair. . . . Who should be waiting there, indeed?

He had black hair but he was plaiting no

love-knot into it. He stood, red collar ashine, amber eyes gleaming, tail swaying with assurance.

I unlocked the door and he swarmed into the interior. *"Hombre,"* I said huskily, "let's go to America."

W<small>E WERE</small> overly optimistic in assuming that because Lobo had been informed verbally of his projected adventure, he would shrug off promptly all allergy to suitcases, traveling bags, and the like. In fact he never did lose the allergy. Any object which looked as if it might contain clothing or possessions packed for a journey meant just one thing to

Lobo: it meant that people were going to go away and leave him. The fear was too deeply rooted, it had flourished too long, it could not be changed. Sometimes I even caught him regarding my briefcase with gravest suspicion.

. . . Felipe carried the last of our bags up the forty-nine steps to where I was struggling to force all our European-Continental possessions into and upon the top of one sedan. It was more or less like the clowns in Ringlings' circus—those several dozen figures who rushed cheering out of one small coupe after it was driven into the ring; except in this case I was trying to get clowns into the car, not take them out.

. . . Irene peered into the depths of the closet where Lobo had been monkishly entombed for the past forty-eight hours.

"Come along, Lobo."

Naturally we always addressed him in Spanish.

"You will accompany us in the car."

The creature bounced into a sitting position and regarded her, eyes rolling, jaws agape. She started to repeat the reassurance, when he gave a dive past her, nearly upsetting her; he plunged through the patio and soared up the several flights of stairs. He emerged from the pink-geranium-smothered hill (again a circus comparison: he reminded me of that character who used to be shot out of a cannon). In mid-trajectory, however, he halted, then flopped to the ground. He had seen all those suitcases. This must mean the end after all. It was not until Irene herself had labored up the steps, opened the car door, and pointed, that he really knew. Jet-propelled by the inexhaustible fuel of his desire, he annihilated gravity and space, and lay gasping atop the highest piled wardrobe container in the rear seat. There was just room for him between the roof and the layers of baggage.

Felipe and Anita came to say their *adiós* but Lobo heeded not. As we drove through the gate and down the highway, I could see him in the mirror. His was also a rear vision, his face turned toward the back window, his ears sagging, as in coma he regarded the Andalucian home existence which he was leaving. He did not even growl at the *Guardia Civil* when they gave us a rifle salute in farewell.

Like all sisters of her sex, Irene had been tempted into a wonderful bargain which in this case consisted of a pair of green shoes, burnished with nailheads, which a local cobbler was going to fashion for her at a price so ridiculously small that she would have insulted her femininity had she not yielded to the temptation. (The fact that she was never able to wear the shoes after she got them is beside the point.) Delivery had been promised for lo these many weeks. She reminded the cobbler forcefully that we were to depart on this day, and that the shoes must be ready: she herself would stop to pick them up.

Thus we drove into Torremolinos for a repeat farewell, since already we had done our duty by grocer, butcher, druggist, and the rest. We parked in a narrow street which, though crowded and dirty, is dignified by the name of Generalissimo Franco, when someone spied Lobo.

"You are about to depart," we were told shrilly. "But look—do you not see? Lobo is in the car."

"Yes, we know."

"But—Lobo?" The voices rose higher. "Do you mean to say—? Is it true? *Madre de Dios!* Is Lobo to accompany you?"

"It is true."

Yells arose on every side. People began to flock from the stores. "María! Pepe! Antonio!

Matilde! Observe! Lobo! In the car! Lobo is to travel in the *coche!* Lobo is going to other nations! . . . Is it true, *Señor?* Is Lobo to go to North America?"

"It is true."

Children pressed in the first rank, adults squeezed behind them, mules came to observe. Not a one of them drew as much as the courtesy of a direct glance from Lobo, who lay collapsed, brassy eyes brooding.

"Enrique! Pablo! Bepa! Lobo—in the car! He goes to many countries! He goes to *los Estados Unidos!*"

. . . We were halfway to Jaén before Lobo emerged from his state of shock sufficiently to threaten two herdsmen who shambled past in the dusk when we were having Sevenses.

Now ensued an interesting series of events both for ourselves, for the black-and-tan beast who ordered our lives, and for sundry hotel-keepers, bartenders, waiters, chambermaids. By custom or legality there was nothing wrong in Lobo's sharing our intimacy. Of course everyone knows that Spain is a back-ward nation. To my notion the nation is nothing like so backward as those States of our Country which prohibit the appearance of dogs in public restaurants. I should much prefer to enjoy my meal with certain dogs under table than with certain people sitting across from me. But little matter now. . . . No eyebrows were raised at Lobo in any café or hostelry throughout Spain or France. (Not until we reached Le Havre, where it seems they are somewhat satiated with American tourists who purchase cute poodle puppies in Paris, transport them to Le Havre to await the sailing of their vessels, and in the past have attempted with futility to housebreak their newly acquired pets upon the best carpeting. I think the refusal of the Le Havre hotel authorities to admit Lobo was rather solidly founded.)

The leash had become an essential in Lobo's traveling equipment, since to his mind all tables were meant to be begged at, and all kitchens to be explored. He accepted his restraint philosophically; and since we were more or less fed up with Spanish cookery (and longed for nothing so much as homemade Spanish rice according to an Iowa recipe, and not at all like the Spanish rice of Spain), Lobo was deeded larger portions of our own fare than had previously come his way.

I shall never forget the fabulous evening in Roquefort, where we deviated from main routes and traveled on back roads, drawn by the mysterious scent of cheese caverns. A certain restaurant there is heavily starred in the guide books. In this place we sat down for the evening meal. Baked Roquefort cheese in light piecrust—I forgot what they call it—was out of this world; and so the steak would have been, the first decent-looking steak I'd seen in many a month. In Andalucía steaks are carved from the very bravest of bulls by means of electric saws and diamond drills.

However, I have neglected to state that I am just as allergic to grilled garlic as was Lobo to steamer trunks. It was my own fault I had not told the waiter. I should have known that they would saturate my sirloin with minute insertions of garlic, drench it with a marinade of garlic, serve it in a garlic sauce. Muttering curses at my own stupidity, I set to work to carve the steak for you-guess-whom.

He was under the table, and put his head up between my knees with the scarf of cloth concealing his eyes and draping his brown mask like a nun's cowl. Promptly at intervals a pink cavern opened, a chunk of beef was dropped in; then, at the stated interval, the pink cavern reopened. It was one of the most interesting disappearing acts I ever saw. That steak was at least three inches thick, and proportionately wide. . . . Lobo seemed fretful when we took him for his evening walk. I think he thought he had had his *canapé* but when did the dinner begin?

His compulsion in the direction of food was something like that endured by Mr. Burl Ives. Mr. Ives spent a lean infancy and childhood amid fellow sharecroppers in southern Illinois, where the butter was spread very thinly—when indeed there was any butter to spread—and where sometimes even the bread was cut much too thinly. In his modern existence as an internationally admired minstrel and actor, Mr. Ives tries vigorously to compensate for the fact that forty years ago there were not enough beans in the pot, and sometimes no bacon at all.

When you are dwelling with Burl, often you are awakened in the middle of the night by a slow thunderous tread in the hall, a squeak and opening and closing of the front door, which is repeated in reverse process some time later. Then comes the rustle of innumerable midnight delicatessen paper bags in the kitchen. In the morning when you go out you find empty cartons with the marks of potato salad and pickled herring still apparent—sausage rinds, seeds, peelings, empty cream containers, soggy receptacles in which various pasties and Boston cream pies have previously been housed. It looks rather as if Henry the Eighth has been entertaining the Yeomen of the Guard in one small kitchen. A few walls away, some three hundred and thirty-three pounds of Ives lie in deep and contented repose.

Lobo also may have had nagging recollection of the sharp-ribbed puppy which was himself, trailing down harsh hillsides above the Mediterranean, and sniffing drearily into ditches which bore not a single morsel of garbage . . . all before his guardian angels conducted him to El Remo.

Carennac is a picturesque village on the Dordogne River in France. There we were ensconced for some time in an ancient abbey turned into hotel, where I worked on my novel even harder than ever, where Irene painted, and Lobo lay on our two old B-10 jackets with a wary eye turned toward the antique Gothic doorway—just in case one of the tourists who sometimes visited the flagged courtyard might intrude.

It was at this place that I requested of Lobo

a written report for the Society for Psychical Research.

In sunset afterglow, weary from toil, the three of us would prowl among shrubbery and walls behind the old chapel. On the first occasion my eye was caught by a coal-black aperture—some sort of tunnel extending down into a dank and mossy area beneath the structure. I was unaccompanied this first time; I went to the car, got a flashlight, and proceeded to examine the chamber. There was nothing in there except a few garden tools, but somehow a storied sepulchral quality was present.

Later that same evening, chaperoned by my two domestic pets, I essayed further investigation. Irene went in boldly enough; Lobo balked at the entrance. He could not be budged. He spread his muscular legs, his deer's feet might have been set in concrete. No matter how I pulled or tugged or persuaded, he was rigid. The hair was up on his back, his ears were raised, and all he said was, "If you want to get me into that place, you'll have to kill me first." Twice at later date I attempted to meet this challenge, and was vanquished. It was not merely darkness that he feared—he had pranced gaily into far blacker holes than this. He had been with me in caves and cellars of various kinds, but into this particular spot he would not venture.

It piqued my curiosity. I sought out the proprietor and asked him the original nature of that room.

"Well," he said. "It was a— The whole place is quite old, you know."

"But what was that subterranean room you now use to put the garden tools in?"

"Oh, it's very difficult to say, *Monsieur*. You see, during the centuries that have elapsed, the room has undoubtedly been used for various purposes." He wriggled uncomfortably.

"O.K.," I said. "Was it the crypt?"

He ducked his head, nodded, fled away. I did not attempt to escort Lobo into any more crypts.

We worked our way up through central and western France toward the inevitable, if temporary, parting in Le Havre. There, in the hotel originally befouled by poodles, our companion was relegated to a dungeon in the basement for one sorry night. Recognizing belatedly that the air was damp and that the place was too uncomfortable for even a toughened veteran like Lobo, I had a bright idea, and bedded him down in the car itself, parked in front of the hotel.

This to Lobo was the height of luxury and satisfaction. That car represented assurance to him; it represented us, it represented his new

life. I saw that in the future it would be unnec-
essary to remove visible bags against the in-
cursion of car thieves. In wildest flight of fancy
I could not envision the bold prowler who
might attempt to force one of those doors,
when inside there existed an arsenal of gleaming teeth and a snarl which would have fright-
ened *El Cid* himself.

Lobo was so entranced with his new lodg-
ings that he refused to budge each morning,
and had to be hauled out bodily. The old jackets were fleecy, security was here, he doted on
security. He knew always that we would come
to the car again. He had a pan of water on the
floor in the front seat; seldom did it seem to be
touched. All night long he dreamed his dreams
and, I firmly believe, wrote his poems and
offered his quiet invocation to the Goddess of
Security.

The eve of our sailing for England was arrived, and we felt that we were leaving our friend in good hands. There was a genial veterinarian who, on viewing Lobo, asserted that he was far too fine an animal to languish in one of the small pens adjacent to the doctor's city office. He explained that in cases like this he always took the dogs to his mother's place in the country. With light hearts we accepted this plan. Lobo wagged and danced, not knowing that we would soon disappear.

Our actual leave-taking occurred abruptly and without planning on my part, since the veterinarian-kennel-keeper had told me that he must have Lobo's rabies-shot certificate. I fetched it over to him, with Lobo along, of course; then we were stricken simultaneously with the same idea. It was only a few hours until I should have to bring him anyway—why not leave him now? Accordingly he cavorted off with the kennel-keeper, confident that *en-*

tremeses were about to be served in the rear.

I returned to the hotel and found Irene come back from shopping. She was grieved. "I didn't get to say goodbye to Lobo."

"Oh, Lobo's fine. The last I saw him the doctor had him on a leash—"

Irene considered for a time. "Just give him a couple of days," she said. "Lobo will have the doctor on a leash."

IN FACT we did not believe that we were leaving him marooned on a linguistic desert island. He had shown a remarkable aptitude for languages. I don't know what all he spoke before we came along. . . . Andaluz was his native tongue. I am sure that he spoke considerable Castilian and perhaps Catalonian, gained from other contacts on the beach. He could not have dwelt long in the polyglot Montemar-El Remo surroundings without at least a smattering of German, Dutch, and French, with a few Scandinavian words thrown in. I think also that he knew some Arabic; he looked as if he did.

Already he had given us a striking demonstration of his ability to absorb English. The month before, in Pau, we endured a rainy afternoon during which all Irene wanted to do was put a new canvas on a stretcher-frame, and all Lobo wanted to do was sleep. We were domiciled in a remodeled chateau on the edge of town, and garages were not far off.

"I think," I called across the living room and into the bedroom where Irene sat on the floor with a mouth full of tacks, "I think that this is a good afternoon for me to take the car down to the garage and have that little matter fixed"—whatever it was—"so I think I'll go now."

I addressed my wife in Midwestern United States, which is our mutual native tongue. Now, mind you, Lobo was sound asleep on the bed; furthermore, neither of us could recall ever having addressed him before in any language except Spanish. In a split second a black-and-tan projectile was fired off the bed and exploded into the target area beside the front door. He stood quivering, bright-eyed, ears up, tail aloft. He said, "Actually I had been intending to sleep the rest of the afternoon, but of course if you're going to the garage—"

We looked at each other helplessly.

"You'd better take him," said Irene. "Perhaps he can help you, when you have trouble with the garage people with your French."

We had not expected to find any other than that which we found on our return after three or four weeks in London, Copenhagen, and West Germany: Lobo was speaking French fluently. We had sent him two or three postcards along the way, and obviously he forgave us for our desertion. ("Why should they send postcards to Lobo?" cried veterinarian and staff. "He cannot read!")

But he could speak French. When the girl assistant brought him out to me at a special rendezvous arranged by telegram from Paris, and which reunion took place within half an hour after our arrival in Le Havre, Lobo was busy in conversation with her. She was talking of the country house, of *Grand'mère*, of the other dogs; and Lobo was joining in, obviously understanding every word she uttered.

We came together. I was assaulted with tongue and claws. I paid my bill and stumbled out. "Let's go right over to the garage," I said, hailing a taxi. "So we can get the car out, and you can have a decent place to sleep tonight."

Like the greater part of Le Havre, the garage area has been rebuilt from scratch since World War II, and this particular garage is a handsome edifice with ramps leading from floor to floor, and room for scores of automobiles on every story.

An old man took us up in an elevator, and we got off at floor Number Five. I unsnapped the leash from Lobo's collar. He raced up and down the aisles of silent parked vehicles.

He found the car quicker than I could have found it—far quicker, I know, than could the old attendant, for he was one of those people who go by card and number. He was still squinting at the ticket and trying to decide in which row the car might be, when Lobo notified us that the car *had* been found, with grunts amplified out of all natural proportion by the peculiar acoustics of the place. I unlocked the door, Lobo flew into the rear seat. The attendant regarded him with something akin to fear, all the way down, as we poked around the short hairpin curves.

Two days later British soil, in the shape of the S.S. *Mauretania*, was treated to its most singular Spanish invasion since the unsuccessful attempt in 1588. . . . Out at sea, I had a little difficulty with the good-looking young assistant-ship's-butcher who was detailed to the care and feeding of canine passengers. I remonstrated about the vast masses of food which were pushed into Lobo's cell.

"But he wants it, sir! He keeps asking for more, he does. I don't know what he does with it all, to be sure. He seems quite hungry. I *did* cut down his rations—"

Even then, there was a certain complication because of Lobo's very strictly conceived toilet habits. The only place allotted to the exercise of dogs was the aft end of the tourist deck; there Lobo and I repaired six or eight times a day. Definitely there was a rule against keeping dogs in one's stateroom—not on the French Line, but on this one. I saw an elderly woman sneaking a suspicious-looking bundle back and forth—something wrapped up in an old raincoat—but even then I didn't protest. A real live Lobo, domiciled in our cabin until we reached New York, would have been just too much.

. . . Trouble was, he had the idea that the deck was a room. It was a room that was not a room. We would go all the way aft, and Lobo would brace himself and stare down at the wake and give grunts as if he recognized the wake of some small vessel in which, many incarnations agone, he had moved through the war-tossed Mediterranean. For several days he simply would not Do Anything. One did not Do Things in rooms, and certainly the deck was a room, because it had a floor. It was a great relief to me when outraged Nature finally threw up her hands, and the deck needed special treatment. Undoubtedly it was a great relief to Lobo as well.

The chief difficulty which I encountered on the voyage was clerical. Not long before we reached New York, I received a message from the old baggagemaster, who insisted that I must come to see him about my dog. Baggagemasters take care of the business of booking dogs aboard steamships. Mr. MacWilliams was a Scotsman with well-established ideas of protocol when it comes to filling out papers.

"I am sorry, sir," he said. "Your papers on your dog are no complete."

"But what's wrong?" We spread the papers out. "Look here, you've got everything: you've got my home address, date of shipment, certificate of good health signed by the French veterinarian within ten days of embarkation. You've got the rabies certificate, you've got—"

His finger indicated one blank square. "You have no put down the *breed* of the dog. Now, will you please to give me the *breed* of the dog?"

I said, "That would be very interesting."

He regarded me disapprovingly through his spectacles. "I can no put *that* down on the paper."

I took a deep breath. Irene and I had discussed Lobo's possible lineage; we knew that he came from the Montemar region, and also that he was prone to worry. "Very well," I said. "If the truth must be known, he is a Montemar Worrier."

The baggagemaster gripped his pencil. "How do you spell it?" Letter by letter, I spelled it out. There is no doubt that Lobo was the first Montemar Worrier—and probably the last—ever to be admitted to the United States.

I was apprehensive about New York. What would happen? Would officials come aboard, would they attempt to take specimens of Lobo's blood? I shuddered to think of what might occur if this came about. Would they pull his eyelids apart? Would they stick things down his throat, and up—elsewhere? I wished that I had some compendium of law through which I might search to gain an idea of exactly what penalty befell the avowed owner of a dog who undertook to carry out a one-dog *pogrom* among Public Health officials.

"But what do I do?" I asked, on that last morning. "Do I wait in the lounge for the officials? Does Lobo ride off on a pile of freight, or does he walk off with me, or what?"

"Just take him along with you," said Mr. MacWilliams. "If yon official wants to see you, he'll find you with no trouble on the quay." Thus Lobo marched on clicking toenails down the gangplank and became an immigrant.

As for the Public Health officials, we saw not hide nor hair of them. The customs officer studied the item on our declaration: *One Lobo. Acquired through self-adoption in Spain. Weight: fifty pounds. Color: black-tan-and-white. Intrinsic value: uncertain*, and then tried to strike up a conversation with Lobo in Gaelic. . . . I still have the papers. Maybe he was never officially admitted after all.

It wasn't until I walked Lobo through the

streets of New York that I began to realize
how like a carefully bred dog he did look. He
was all of a pattern, he didn't look like a mon-
grel. His doe-colored stockings were all of the
same size, his tan mask well-balanced; there
was the set and feeling of a breed about him.
No mere ascribing of possible parentage
through the process of free love among German shepherds, Dobermans, and hounds
seemed to suffice. It wasn't until quite a time
afterward, when—Lobo-less—Irene and I ven-
tured on back roads of the Basque country,
that we came to know what he was in fact,
although it had been suggested a time or two.

He was a Basque shepherd. If we saw one
we saw forty Lobos in the Basque country.
We saw two or three that could have been his
litter-mates; but I fear that I shall never own
another Basque shepherd. . . .

How Lobo's father ever found his way

down the long rugged Iberian Peninsula to Mediterranean shores, I leave to be decided by the canine archaeologists, ethnologists, genealogists, and historians who should deal with this fascinating subject in the future. As it was, in New York people kept coming up to me on the street and wanting to know what kind of dog that was. I always said that he was a Montemar Worrier, which satisfied in every case. One old lady informed me that indeed that's what he was—a Montemar Worrier—she remembered now; her sister used to have one of those.

Lobo and I left Irene surrounded by doting grandchildren in Westchester, and sought Florida quickly. Again we had the ton of baggage to be transported; but this time Lobo could share the front seat with me; although now, on alien shores, he had a propensity for putting his head in my lap. This I regarded as a safety hazard. We had a few words and cuffs

on the subject; after that he behaved properly
—thrusting his head out of the right window,
and observing critically the Howard Johnson
edifices along the Jersey Turnpike.

In Maryland an interesting experience befell when—perforce, of necessity, as is the
habit of motorists—I decided suddenly to stop
by the wayside and take a stroll into a
thicketed area. Lobo tumbled out along with
me, and went around through the woodland
like a runaway jeep, except that he made more
noise about it. I discovered that his grunts
were not all recognition grunts (or maybe
they were: this reincarnation idea, you see, although he had never heard of Bridey
Murphy). They were also inquisitive grunts.

"Goodness sake, what is this—what are all
these trees? What are all these bushes? What
are all these smells? Ah-ha, above all, the
smells! Well, what is this, anyway?"

The idea struck me full force. It is a strange

experience to proceed into the mild forests of Maryland, with a dog of obvious maturity, and realize that the dog has never been in *woods* before.

There are no woods in the locality from which Lobo sprang. There are a few trees bordering gardens, a very few bordering the roads; there are olive groves, and some tiny groves of poplars grown as a crop. Nothing more. The rest is rocks, wasteland, low tough herbage. No thickets, no bushes, no wild brakes.

There was something touching about all this . . . I wondered how he would go plunging through the bit of Florida jungle which has not been Yankeeized, and which we own. (He went plunging, all right. He came home twice without his collar.)

Few bridegrooms ever lugged their brides across fabled thresholds with more excitement

than that with which I escorted Lobo to our beach, once we were safe on Siesta Key. His hard racing feet tore the white packed sand. . . . Birds, birds! He was after them full pelt. Of course I knew that he could never catch one; but he did not know that, and never learned the fact. Water would smash as he struck it, the birds would go squawking. . . .

Coconuts were more vulnerable to his attack. A green coconut, shell and all, washed up on the beach, is a heavisome thing, God wot. To me they weighed just as much as so many atomic bombs, but to Lobo they were peanuts. How he got his jaws around them I'll never know, but he did. Not only did he get his jaws around them, but he would bear them off at full gallop. I have seen him do this with coconuts which weighed roughly a quarter of Lobo's own weight. If you are a man of ordinary size, try clamping a forty-pound burden in your jaws, and dashing off with it.

Lobo had several private coconut hoards: one under pines on the beach, a couple among palms out in the yard. These treasured toys were doled out to him in frolicksome moments. But unfortunately coconuts were not the only objects against which he now directed his threat.

The old parable of rags to riches had come true again. In Spain a penniless beggar, Lobo was tolerant as to disposition. He drew no property lines around El Remo or the Montemar. Let who would come and go, was his philosophy.

Not so after he had acquired a seaside home in Florida, with a couple of cars thrown in. He was more avaricious than Hetty Green, more savage than Simon Girty, less charitable than Ebenezer Scrooge.

"Good grief!" he would roar at the top of his lungs, dashing through the gallery and across the living room and out to the porch, slashing the rugs as he came. "Look out there on the beach! There's an old man walking on *my beach*. I can't *stand* this. He needs to be torn limb from limb! Please open the door and let me out! I want to go down there and *assassinate* him—"

I thought of the smug but discerning Civil Guard, far back in the Province of Málaga, who observed, "Lobo is very rich now." In vain did I explain, cajole, and set examples of hospitality and benevolence. He was far gone into a most predatory sort of snobbery. If people didn't belong on his property, they didn't belong on it. That went for practically all humans.

As for dogs, he would pay ardent court to those females who were in a courting mood; would calmly ignore other females or the especial type of spinsters with which the

canine world is so frequently blessed. But—a
male dog— I was kept busy snatching at Lobo's
collar, and explaining to the world that he was
not truly vicious—he was just savage, and had
an exaggerated sense of property rights and
controls.

Our two small grandsons came with their
parents to spend the Christmas holidays, and
we watched Lobo narrowly. I heard him
growl just once. He had an ear infection and
Mike, the elder, pulled his sore ear. I explained
to Mike, and he did not do this again. On the
other hand, I came in one day to find the
smaller boy in his play pen with Lobo lying
just outside the wooden bars. Tommy had fas-
tened his grubby mitts on Lobo's muzzle, and
was kneading flesh and nostrils energetically.
Lobo was not uttering a sound, nor was he
trying to move away; he was just taking it
from the baby. We breathed more easily after
that.

LOBO

As if to compensate for whatever inconvenience his highhanded defense of the home caused us, Lobo now offered assistance of an acceptable kind. Heart and soul he became dedicated to helping me in my work.

In Spain he had paid but little heed: I went out each day in the car with my portable typewriter installed on a folding chair which served as table. I took a basket of lunch, bottle of wine, my briefcase and whatever reference books had been selected for the day's activity. That was all right with Lobo; most of the time he was content to remain at home, lying on cool tiles, leisurely inspecting Irene's painting as it progressed.

But *Andersonville* had grown from an originally promised one-hundred-and-fifty-thousand-word novel into a novel of a projected three-hundred-and-fifty-thousand words. . . . There are such things as deadlines in the publishing business; mechanical details of manufacturing have to be set up in advance; thus they were starting to put the book into type long before I had finished it. Uneasy lies the head of an author under such circumstances. . . .

I dared not let a day pass without a substantial amount accomplished, and sometimes I was very near the breaking point. Friends and relatives urged me to slow down, take a trip, go away somewhere—but I knew I'd be working every day I was gone, so what could be gained in going?

I began to find Lobo in the car each morning when I went to the garage. He sensed that I needed help and was willing to offer such as he could give. The house was unendurable as

a workplace most of the time, even with the
telephones shut off, because of people who
came to the door, and my vulnerability to such
interruptions. I had to drive afield, usually into
the Myakka wilderness east of Sarasota, or to
a lonely spot down the Tamiami Trail where
I could not be reached or interfered with.

I took to fetching along Lobo's lunch as well
as my own. He never interfered with my typ-
ing; I left the rear door open when parked in
the shade, and Lobo could hop in and out as
the spirit moved him. There was only one difficulty: forever he was coming back hobbling
from the effects of sandspurs. I would have to
extract myself from behind the typewriter and
succor the needy—always rewarded by a slob-
bery tongue well applied.

He did feel that we should sleep together
when we took our naps. It was disconcerting
to be aroused from stupor by the crushing

blow of his compact body as he flung himself over the seat on top of me.

There came a day when I thought I could work no more. My head ached, my eyes hurt, my finger tips were filmy. I had been at it daily, without exception, for over fifteen months. *You can't finish*, evil voices were crying. *You can't. You can't. Don't try. It's too much. It's too big. It's too long. It's too tiring. You can't do it. You're no stronger than anyone else. Flesh and brain can endure only so much. Emotions break, and discipline vanishes, and you're tired, tired, tired.*

I managed to back the car out of the garage, but couldn't turn it away toward the driveway from the live-oak shade. Lobo was in the rear seat. Over on the right-hand side of the front seat, the typewriter waited on its stand—grimly, implacably, presenting that threatening countenance which typewriters have forever turned toward exhausted writers. I put my head back on the seat and was close to tears.

Then there came a heavy breathing in my ear. A nose was thrust close.

"Lobo, what shall I do?" My own voice sounded far away and flogged. "I can't go on. What shall I do—quit? Quit for a while, try later, put the book off? What shall I do?"

With a single bound he was over the ridge. He was in the front seat, sitting bolt upright behind the typewriter, staring ahead. Then he swung his head to the left, grinned, rolled his eyes.

"You mean," I faltered, "that I've got to go to work anyway? That I've got to go out in the car and at least try to do *something*?"

He bent down, put his head on the seat, pushed with his hind legs, stood on his head, and smashed over across my lap.

"O.K.," I groaned. Away we drove. I

wrote twenty-seven hundred words in the next two hours or so. They were pretty good words—or so at least some of the critics thought who quoted them later.

. . . The Pulitzer Prize seemed a long way off in those days; so did the films, so did the critical response, so did the fortune which would be earned for booksellers, publishers, the Federal Government, the book clubs, editors, agents, and even myself. But Lobo knew. Assuredly he knew.

It was pretty tough on Irene, managing him when I was away. I had to go back to the Andersonville region several times; there was a research trip to Mississippi, and so on. During each of these periods Lobo appointed himself High Sheriff of Siesta Key, and lay most of the time either at Irene's feet or upon her bed. The mildest step of dry cleaner, spring-water man, or mere casual caller was sufficient to bring him into a defensive attitude similar to that of the Iberian women who tore out their hair to braid it for bowstrings. Not the most thorny commando in the world could have entered the house without first riddling Lobo with his burp gun.

Once Irene had flu while I was gone, and our friend and family doctor, Tom Garrett, came to attend her. Tom went out of that bedroom faster than he came in. This was not even reasonable, because Lobo knew Tom, and tolerated him socially. But I was gone, and he was *pro tem* guardian of bed, board, and belfry.

There was nothing sensible in his attitude, and I am not apologizing for him. In short, he was a damn nuisance about this sort of thing. No dog should behave in such wise. But I had come to the terrifying opinion that Lobo was not actually a dog.

LOBO

I asked him about it one day, when we were coming home from work.

"Is it true," I inquired in my most carefully constructed Spanish, which I fear isn't very carefully constructed, but was always understandable to Lobo, "is it true that you are not in fact a dog, but are actually a king of the Moors?"

He had the answer to that one too. He stood on his head, to show me that he was a veritable emperor of the Moors.

He had spent all his years, uncertain though they were as to number, in trying to find a home of his own and people of his own. He had found them, and now nothing in the world must interfere with his possession of them.

. . . Did he ever dream of the white-washed farmhouses, the noisy village street, the mules, the creaking carts, the green-uni-formed constabulary he had left thousands of miles behind? An echo was there one night for him to hear; he heard it and responded.

We were sitting in the living room with friends, and Lobo was flat on his back, sound asleep on our bed at the other end of the house, all four paws dangling in the air. I knew this because I had seen him so a few minutes before. . . . People were asking about the Holy Week processions current throughout Spain, and we were trying to give a description—trying to make them see the images with their jewels, the flare of ten thousand candles, the robed figures walking, the drums and bugles and weird Moorish pipes coming on ahead.

"Why," I said, "I have an album, a recording made over there. The Girl With the Combs—a fat gypsy woman who is one of the finest *saeta* singers in Spain. It sounds like the real stuff. Let me play it for you—"

I put on the record. First there came the

throb and shuffle of feet. You could imagine
the heavy *paso* being lifted onto thirty or forty
shoulders, the striving bodies, the ragged cord-
soled sandals scraping uneven pavement stones.
You could hear bugles beginning to talk, the
pound of drums as slatternly fifteen-year-old
musicians in their baggy khaki uniforms rolled
and marched. *La niña* started in with her chant.
Her voice swept on high, the traditional arrow
of song above the sound of marchers, the military hullabaloo, the religious illusion.

Then another sound intermingled with this,
and it did not come from the Hi-Fi. It was a
series of grunts, approaching steadily up the
long hall which led from our bedrooms. *Unh,
unh, unh, unh, unh?* Here he came, recognition sounds floating ahead.

Unh, unh, unh, unh?

He was in the middle of the living room,
ears lifted, body tensed, face turned toward

the corner where the instrument lived. The gypsy's voice soared on; she wailed about the agony of Our Dear Lord; bugles blatted, drums throbbed.

Unh, unh, unh, unh? He was gone into the corner to stand close to the amplifier, and he was still sniffing, but his nose told him nothing, *nada*.

He was not home, he was not back in Spain. Oh, yes, this was home, but . . . there was a memory, he had heard sounds . . . where did they come from? Because there was no actuality here. No smell. Only the sounds which he had learned in puppyhood. . . . Finally he collapsed, flopped on the floor, went to sleep, paid no more heed.

Once I knew and loved a man who was a notorious tightwad. He was often inconsiderate of others—he was not even very good in his profession, nor very dependable, although he managed to make quite a lot of money. He did not ever do little thoughtful things for other people, he seldom repaid favors to friends, he did not always sacrifice himself too sublimely on community projects. Yet when he died the whole town wept. Everybody adored him, no one knew quite why. Everyone missed him; they miss him still.

Thus it was with Lobo. He was a gourmand; he set a high record for selfishness; he was far too savage for comfort; he was always wanting to go in and out of doors just because he wanted to go in and out of doors. He was a thief: he stole a roast in New York, a steak in Sarasota, two pounds of ground beef at La Verdad. He lay on beds, he begged at table, he left a cloud of shed hairs wherever he moved —cars and furniture were coated with them. (Months after he left us, I was still picking black white-tipped hairs off the ceiling of one automobile—and how they ever got there is more than I know. I suppose it was when he stood on his head and waved his tail in the air.)

Lobo gave no alarms of fire. So far as I know he never saved a child from drowning, or a traveler from freezing to death in the snow. He bit inoffensive Other Dogs. He lay right in the middle of all the main avenues, and you were forever falling over him.

By ordinary standards of polite conduct, Lobo was a mess. Yet the majesty and mystery which he exuded reached far. People were mad for him, even the ones he growled at.

Friends would call up with informal invitations to dinner, and were always careful to state that Lobo was especially included. Once established in the kitchen—say, at Ed Beattie's —he got in the maid's way every minute, and Mardelle loved it.

. . . He went along with me to Newtown

areas where most of the Sarasota servants live, to help take the laundry to Hattie May. Immediately soft dusky voices would speak lovingly from neighboring porches. "Why, there's Lobo. Hello, Lobo. Don't you remember me, Lobo?" His ears would sprout, nostrils sniff in awareness, his saffron eyes would be polished and sharp.

He knew far too much for his own good and for my own. He knew on that last morning, the eighth of August, when I left him at the vet's in Scarsdale, New York. We were up there temporarily; we had to be in order to attend to the preliminaries of publishing *Andersonville*.

This was just a routine thing: he seemed to need worming attention again, I would leave him to be wormed. But the vet heard a suspicious cough, and asked a few questions, and said he should like to make some tests. The

next day we heard the verdict: heartworms—
the parasites which dwell in subtropical re-
gions, but now I hear are making their wicked
way North.

"It won't be much," the doctor said. "I'll
start his series of shots . . . he'll have to be
here all of this week, and next week you can
bring him in every other day."

. . . He didn't want to be left there. Lobo
said, "Please do not leave me. There is something I fear," and he twisted in circles at the
end of his leash, and kept thrusting his head
between my legs, and quivering. It hurts like
to hell to remember that now. . . . They
gave him the first shot that evening, and it
killed him *pronto*.

Nobody could understand. The doctor got
another doctor out of bed in the dead of night.
They worked hard, they called the laboratory
from which the serum had come. Nothing was

wrong with it. They got chemists out of bed and talked to them. But nothing could be done, although they tried to do everything.

The next day there was an autopsy, and we thought of the weird illnesses which had seemed to possess Lobo at La Verdad. Still that wasn't all the answer, and we have never found some of the answer yet.

Other veterinary physicians must have cried in the past; but it so happens that that was the first time I ever saw one do so.

We took Lobo up to the Hartsdale Canine Cemetery and put him into the hillside. There he lies, the eight-thousand-eight-hundred-and-ninety-first pet to sleep there. He has his stone —in Spanish, of course. It says: *Adiós, Amigo*.

The people at the place have been catering to bereaved humans for a long time, and so they know just what to do. They put flowers on his grave in summer and evergreens in winter. There he rests in the clutch of his adopted land—adopted through choice, no one can gainsay that.

So we left him on that tenth of August, and I took Irene home. Then I did what a good many other men would have done: I headed for the nearest bar.

It happened to be Buddy Kennedy's bar on Central Avenue. When Buddy saw my face he knew there was very bad news. Lobo used to go in there with me, and everyone knew him. Buddy is sentimental, like most ex-vaude-villians; we had our tears together.

An amiable Irishwoman was sipping a beer down the bar. She said, "You know, I'd like to tell you something. I dearly loved a mutt one time; he came to my door in the snow, half-starved, and I took him in, and he brought the sunshine into my life. When he died I couldn't take it. Our priest was an old family friend, and I said to the priest, 'But why did my Paddy have to be run over? I loved him so—I wanted him with me always.' And the priest said, 'Daughter, you never really *had* your Paddy dog. You never *owned* him. He was loaned to you by God, as are all good people and beasts. And God needed him somewhere else, perhaps, to help some other people as he helped you. So he took him back.' "

I could barely thank the woman, but the comfort of her little story stayed with me. That is the way I began to think of Lobo then; that is the way I think of him now, and always shall. A strange and endearing form of Spanish Lend-Lease. . . . Paws across the sea, and all that sort of thing.

ABOUT THE AUTHOR

MacKinlay Kantor was born in Webster City, Iowa, February 4, 1904. He started to write seriously at the age of sixteen, and his first novel was published in 1928. Since then thirty-one of his books have been appreciated by readers in America and abroad: verse, collections of short stories and novelettes, juvenile books, histories, and many novels, with a crowning achievement in the latter field—the monumental *Andersonville*, for which the author was awarded the Pulitzer Prize. MacKinlay Kantor's accomplishments include one of the most famous motion pictures of all time, *The Best Years of Our Lives*, for which he wrote the original story. By no means solely devoted to the art of authorship, Mr. Kantor has achieved combat experience in two wars, and was personally decorated by the commander of the United States Air Force.

Irene Layne, who illustrated *Lobo*, is the author's wife. They are the parents of Layne Shroder, who in 1957 published her first novel. Their son Thomas M. Kantor is a former Air Force flyer.

The home of the Kantors is at Sarasota, Florida, although in recent years they have lived often abroad.